For Kalum,Zackary and Timothy.

Copyright © 2021 by M.M Hobs

First paperback edition November 2021

Book design and illustrations by M.M Hobs

ISBN 978-1-3999-0765-1 (Paperback)
Independently published by M.M Hobs
Distributions Amazon KDP
www.mmhobs.co.uk

Penguin

in the

Window

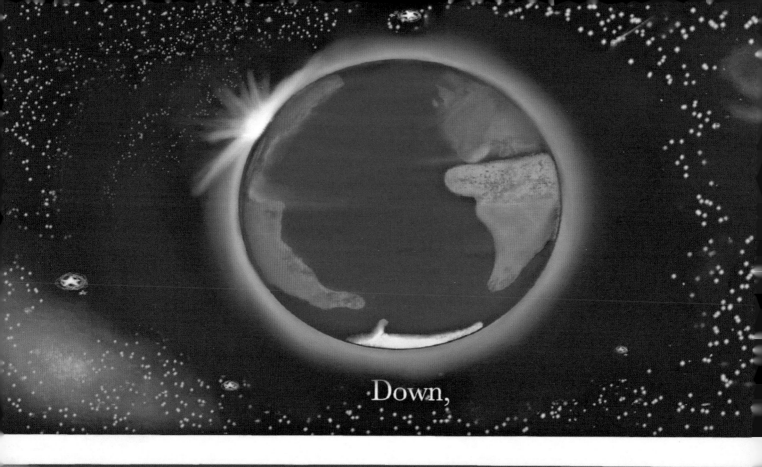

Down,

Down,

DOWN!

Stop!

Look...

I

dive,

I am diving,

I am the diving Penguin.

I swim

and swim

and swim

and swim.

I, I,

I, I...

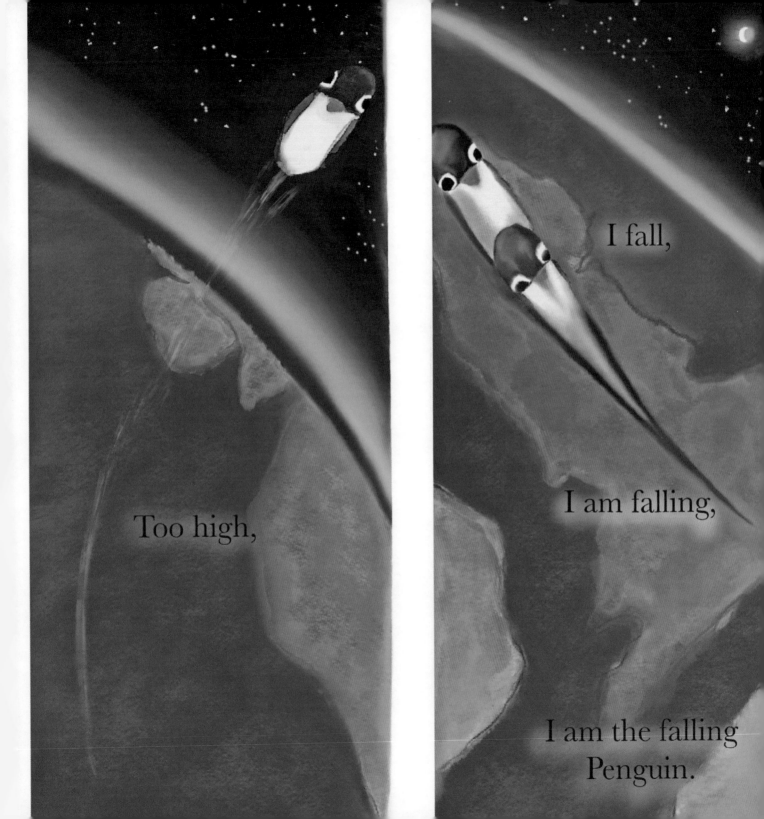

Too high,

I fall,

I am falling,

I am the falling
Penguin.

I...

I am lost!

I am the lost Penguin in the window.

I am worried,

I am panicking,

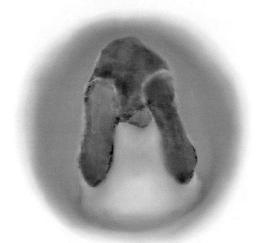

I am scared.

I am the scared Penguin in the window.

I remember,

I wonder,

I search.

I am the searching Penguin in the window

I wait

and wait

and wait

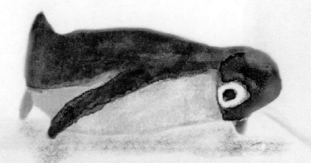

and WA...

WAVE! I am waving.
I am the waving Penguin
in the window.

I see, I smile,

I laugh.

I am laughing. I am the laughing Penguin in the window.

I hear, I listen, I dance.

I am the dancing Penguin in the window.

I change and change

and change and change.
I am the changing Penguin in the window.

I watch, I reflect, I respect.

I am the respectful
Penguin in the window.

I wake,

I sneak, I peek,   I celebrate.

I am the celebrating Penguin in the window.

I stop, I am still, I am here.

I am….PENGUIN IN THE
WINDOW!

I am sleepy, I am tired, I am...

I am thankful, I am kind, I am bonnie,

I am witty, I am clever, I am treasured,

I am capable, I am worthy, I am unique, I am enough

I am humble, I am precious, I am brave,

...llous I am courageous,

I am ...

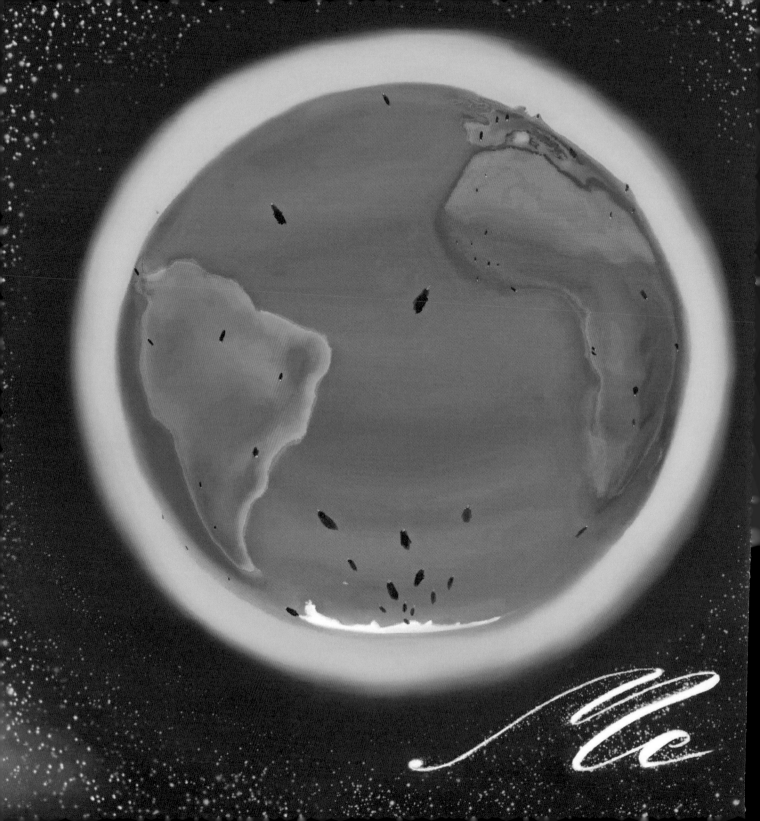

Printed in Great Britain
by Amazon